Introducing

Ocean Olly Octopus

and his underwater friends

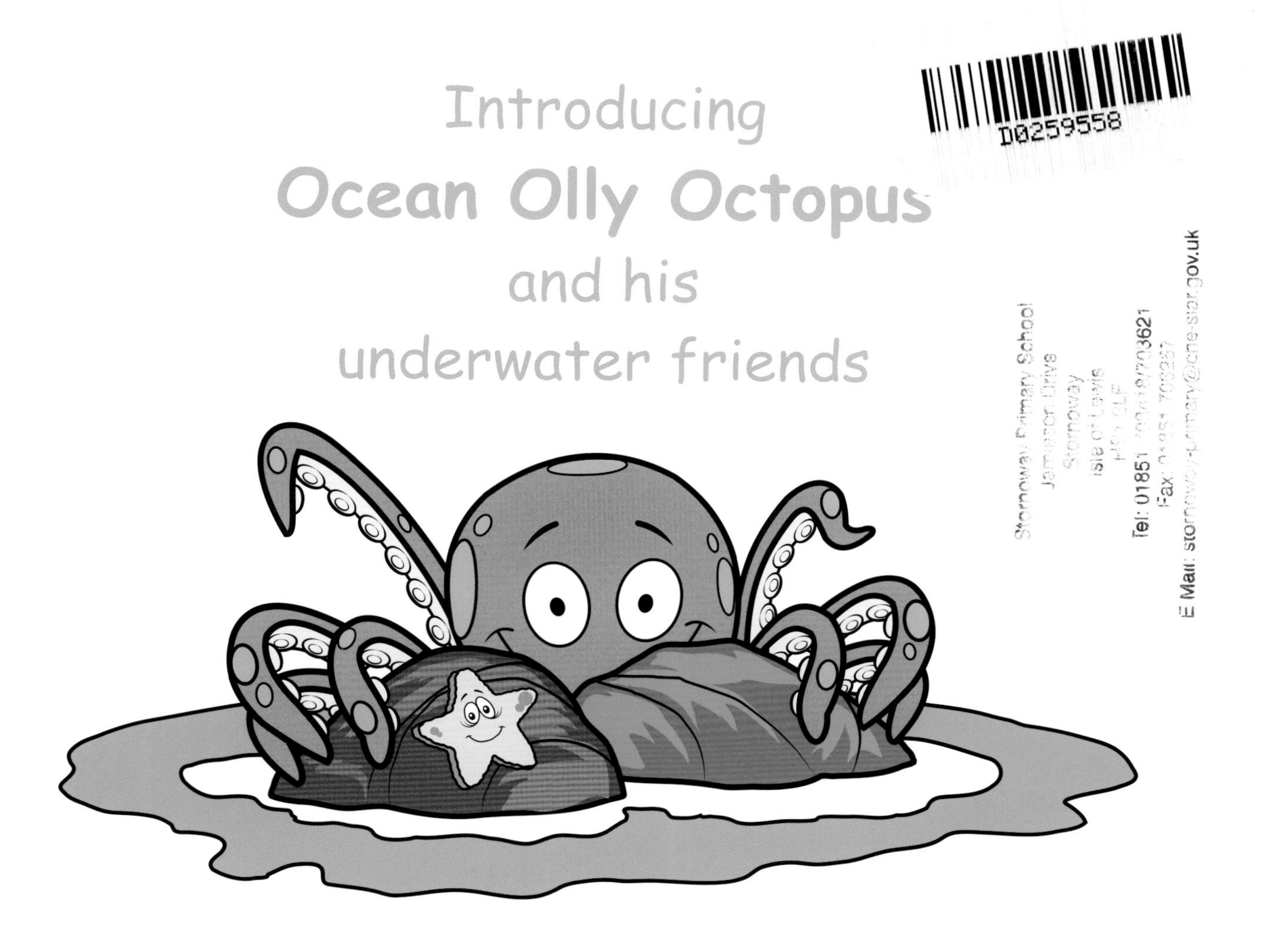

OLLY MEETS A SHARK

Publisher: Padraigin Promotions

By Patricia Melia - Illustrator Garry Thorburn

Olly Octopus, who was young, curious and cheeky, lived with his family inside an old wreck. A long, long time ago a ship was shipwrecked. It sank down on to some rocks on the sea bed. It landed just next to the rocks where Olly's family lived. Olly's great grandparents decided to make their home inside the wreck.

One morning, as Olly was playing around his home,
he saw an unusual fish swimming nearby.
It was very brightly coloured.
Olly had never seen such a brightly coloured fish before.
He was very curious. As the fish swam away,
Olly decided to swim alongside it to have a
closer look. When the fish noticed Olly he said,
"I know who you are. You're an octopus and you live
on the bottom of the ocean. What a funny looking
creature you are." "Yes, I'm an octopus.
My name is Olly Octopus," Olly replied.
He was very surprised to be called 'funny looking.'
"I was just about to ask who you are," he said.
"I've never seen such bright colours before."

"Well, since you ask," replied the fish,
"my name is Paddy Parrotfish. Where I come from,
all fish are brightly coloured. What's more, because
we are special, we live in a very special place not far
from here. Sometimes we can even change our colour."
"Well, I have eight tentacles," Olly replied,
"and what's more," he continued cheekily,
"I can also change colours, though not as
brightly as you can," he admitted.
Paddy Parrotfish was very sensible.
He understood that not all creatures were
the same size, shape or colour.
Paddy decided he would like to be friends with
this octopus called Olly.

1
2
3
4
5
6
7
8

"Would you like to see where I live?" Paddy asked Olly.
"Come with me and I'll show you my home.
It's called a coral reef.
I'll show you my little sister Polly.
I'll show you all my friends. It's over there."
He wiggled his brightly coloured fin towards
a ridge of rock in the distance.
Olly thought for a moment. . . "Well," he said,
"I should really ask my parents first, as I'm not
allowed to leave the wreck without permission.
Er. . . Oh. . . I suppose it will be
alright - as I'm going with you."
So they both set off together.
When they reached the top of the ridge, Olly looked
down the other side. He couldn't believe his eyes!

As Paddy had said, there were fish of
every size, shape and colour.
There were some striped fish, some spotted
fish and some you could see right through,
called transparent fish. Each one was more
colourful than the next. They were all darting
in and out of the coral reef.
Olly gazed in wonder at the brightly coloured fish
darting happily around. Then he noticed that they
were starting to dart about in a frightened way,
looking for places to hide.
"Paddy, what's happening?" Olly asked.
Paddy realised quickly what the problem was.
"Quick, follow me under this rock ledge.
Polly, you too," he ordered.
They all made it - just in time.

A giant creature appeared. It looked VERY fierce. It had rows of sharp pointed teeth and it had a very angry expression. It swam quite close by the place where Olly, Polly and Paddy were hiding. Olly was very frightened and squeezed himself farther under the rock. He wished that he had never left the safety of his home on the wreck.

THE GIANT CREATURE SEEMED TO LOOK STRAIGHT AT WHERE OLLY, POLLY AND PADDY WERE HIDING!

Meanwhile, back at the wreck, Olly's mum Orla and dad Oscar had missed him. They were searching frantically for him. They knew all too well the dangers of straying too far from home.

Olly's little sister Olivia was crying.
She told her parents she had seen Olly talking
to a strange, brightly coloured fish.
This news made them sad and disappointed.
They realised that Olly had gone off without asking them.
He could be lost! However, Oscar knew all about
the brightly coloured fish that lived over on the
coral reef. So Oscar and Orla set off together to find him.
When they finally arrived at the coral reef,
Oscar noticed, with surprise, that there were far
fewer fish than usual swimming about. Then they saw
Olly, Polly and Paddy hiding under a rock.
Then they saw the reason why! There, in front of them,
was the fiercest shark they had ever seen.

From under the rock, Olly spotted his parents and
began to cry for help. His dad called out to everyone,
"Stay where you are, don't move! Leave this to me.
I know how to deal with this danger."
Oscar then distracted the shark's attention
away from all the others by swimming out in front of it.

SUDDENLY THE SHARK SEEMED ABOUT TO ATTACK!

Oscar then used his secret weapon, which he had
hidden in his body - a dark, inky fluid that
an octopus can squirt whenever there is danger.
Oscar squirted this at the shark swimming towards him.
The inky fluid made the water very dark.
This confused and upset the shark.
He swam away very quickly.
"Phew! It's safe now," shouted Oscar.
"The danger has passed."

Everyone was very relieved.
Olly was so happy to see his parents.
He promised them he would never, ever wander
off again without asking. They waved goodbye to Paddy
as they set off together for home. All the other fish
darted happily around the reef. As a special thanks
to Oscar for helping them to escape from danger,
the fish made a wonderful, brightly coloured display.
They changed colours time and time again.
It was just like watching a fireworks display.

Everyone arrived home safely. Olly was so pleased to
be home that he even gave his little sister
Olivia a big hug, which made her smile.
So they had a little party and invited Grandpa along,
to celebrate Olly's safe return home.

OLLY
meets a
SHARK

First published in soft back in the UK by
Padraigin Promotions in 2010
Printed in Lancashire UK

Padraigin Promotions, 27 Bolton Road, Darwen, Lancashire BB3 1DF
www.Ollyoctopus.com

ISBN Number 978-0-9564946-0-3

Writer Patricia Melia

Illustrator Garry Thorburn